me
myself
& I

by **T. Bugbird**

Designed by **Annie Simpson**

Illustrations by **Charlotte Stratford**

With thanks to **Hope Bicknell**

Copyright © 2008

make believe ideas ltd

27 Castle Street, Berkhamsted, Herts, HP4 2DW

Manufactured in China

me *myself* & I

...*is all about* **you,**
what you **think** *and what you* **do.**
Take the **test,** *total your* **scores,**
then check out the **results.**
Do you agree? *Well, maybe.*
It's just for **fun,**
so **whatever** *you feel,*
love *who you are*
and keep it **real!**

take the test!

what's
inside...?

contents

contents

contents

are you the life of the party?

Choose from A, B, or C, then total your results and turn the page!

1

It's the weekend and all your friends are out of town. What do you do?

A Trail your sis and her buddies all weekend. OK, hanging out with your kid sister is bad for your rep but it's better than being stuck with the 'rents!

B Nothing. Having time out alone rocks! You're psyched at the thought of two whole days of me, myself, and I!

C Take the opportunity to hang out with your family. Your mom and dad — and even your little sister — can be quite cool when you give them a chance!

2

Your BF has bagged tickets to a concert this evening—but the show starts in an hour and you're totally unprepared! Yikes! How do you react?

A You're psyched! There's no way you'll miss the concert! Run for the bus and you might make it before the opening act is taking its final bow!

B She may be pumped, but you're gonna pass. Last-minute surprises always freak you out. You need to be prepared or you just can't relax!

C Wow — your friend is so thoughtful! You'd love to go, but you'll consult your parents first. With their help you might make it to the concert AND finish your school work!

3

Your sister and her friends are goofing around while you're trying to study! Do you . . .

A Join in? It looks like they're having fun!

B Bawl them out for disturbing your study time?

C Ask them to move the party to another room — or house? But it looks like they're having a blast, so maybe you'll join them later!

4

What do you think of first when choosing a new pair of shoes?

A Can I dance in them?

B Do they look comfortable?

C Will they go with the rest of my clothes?

quiz ?

quiet time

5 *Is it important to be one of the "in" crowd at school?*

A Absolutely. The uber-cool crowd always know where the best parties are.

B Not at all; it's much better to be your own person and not feel pressured to look or behave in a certain way.

C The most important thing is to feel relaxed and happy whoever your friends are — if they are "in," great, if not, who cares?

6 *Your classmates are auditioning for "Dance Factor," the hot new talent show! They need a girl to make up their group and ask you. How do you react?*

A What an amazing opportunity! You don't need to think about it. It's a "YES!"

B You'd kinda like to go for it but don't think you'd be comfortable performing in front of judges. And you'd hate to mess things up and let your friends down. So it's a "no."

C Sounds great but you need details! When is it? Where is it? What kind of dance are they planning? When are you going to practice? And what's the prize? It's a big decision so you'll need some time to think about it.

7 *What's the best part of a vacation?*

A Discovering new places and meeting new people. The best vacations are full of adventures.

B Vacations are great, but the best part is coming home and sleeping in my own bed.

C There's no best part — all vacations are different and special in their own way.

8 *Congrats! You've won a major competition. Which prize do you choose?*

A Free clothes for a year

B A bedroom makeover

C A family vacation in Florida

Mostly As, Bs, or Cs? Count 'em up then flip over the page.

9

what's your score?

are you the life of the party?

mostly As

Wow, you really are the life of the party! You're full of fun and rarely let practicalities get in the way of fun times. It's great to have such a positive attitude, but you don't always think before you act. Remember, you rarely have to say "yes" to invitations or offers right away. Who knows, your friends may respect you more if you take time out to make decisions, or even opt to chill out by yourself once in a while.

mostly Bs

You really are a stay-home kind of girl. You love your own company and appreciate time with your family. You plan in advance and don't like things to change at the last minute. Having confidence in just being you is great, but don't shut yourself off from the great opportunities life has to offer. Let your hair down once in a while, or try something new just for fun!

mostly Cs

You have a great, balanced attitude. You love time with your friends *and* time alone. You rarely act without thinking things through first, but are not afraid of new experiences. You try your best to have time for others and are considerate of their feelings. This level-headed outlook probably means you're the first person your friends come to for advice. Just don't forget to think about yourself from time to time — you're not super-girl!

top 10

soundtrack to the movie of my life

Which songs would you choose?

1
2
3
4
5
6
7
8
9
10

the funny part

the sad part

the happy ending

FASHION FILE

so now!

GOING UP

GOING DOWN

so last year!

what
kind of
snack
are
you?

Are you as sweet as chocolate, as soft as a bagel, or full of fruity energy and always on the go? There's only one way to find out! Follow the arrows and see just how yummy you really are!

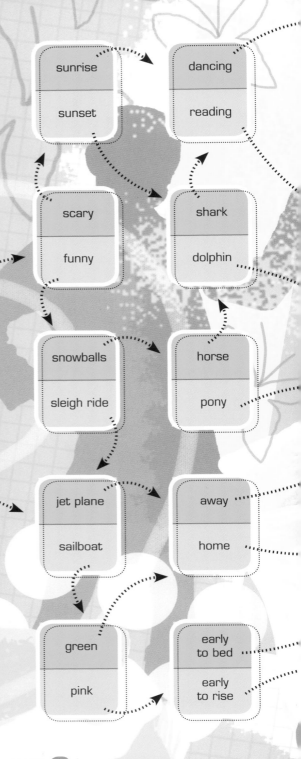

sunrise
sunset

dancing
reading

scary
funny

shark
dolphin

salt
sugar

snowballs
sleigh ride

horse
pony

jet plane
sailboat

away
home

green
pink

early to bed
early to rise

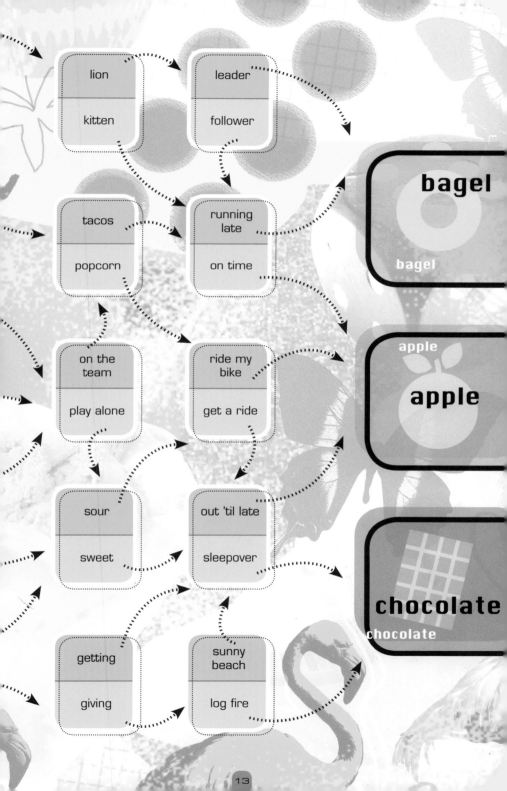

lion / kitten

leader / follower

tacos / popcorn

running late / on time

bagel
bagel

on the team / play alone

ride my bike / get a ride

apple
apple

sour / sweet

out 'til late / sleepover

chocolate
chocolate

getting / giving

sunny beach / log fire

13

bagel

bagel

You sometimes feel you're going around in circles but that's 'cuz you're sooo busy and always on the go! You can appear quite tough, but on the inside you're warm and soft!

apple

apple

Wow — you've got so much energy! You get bored really easily and love all sorts of sports, dancing, and anything that means not having to stay still in one place! You're super-organized and love trying new things.

chocolate

chocolate

You are sweet and kind and love to cheer up your friends when they're feeling down. When you're not treating your friends, you love nothing more than curling up in front of the TV or reading your favorite books.

are you a
fool for fashion

Read each question, and every time you agree, shade in the number of empty boxes listed in brackets after it. Start at the bottom of the Fashionometer. How high will your "trendperature" rise?

The new season's fashions always look better than the last. **(3)**

I hate fancy-dress parties because everyone looks so stupid. **(2)**

Shopping is better than the movies. **(1)**

The most important thing about a winter coat is that it looks good. **(2)**

If I see my fave celebs wearing something, I want it too! **(3)**

It's great to share clothes with your friends. **(1)**

I love to dress up for parties. **(2)**

I'd love a Chihuahua to carry in my purse. **(3)**

I think celebrities who are slammed for their dress sense should try harder. **(2)**

I get bored with my clothes really quickly. **(3)**

I've had my favorite sweater for years. **(1)**

In the old days, no-one had style! **(3)**

As soon as an outfit goes out of style, I ditch it. **(3)**

I get really upset if someone is wearing the same outfit as me. **(2)**

It's fun to mix up trends and looks from different seasons. **(1)**

I love reading the best/worst-dressed lists in magazines. **(2)**

I change my hairstyle every week. **(3)**

Sometimes I think the latest trends look really funny. **(1)**

31+
Fashion victim! Enjoy fashion, but remember, it's great to be yourself.

15 - 30
You have your own style. Celebrate it!

up to 14
Totally grounded! But don't fear fashion!

| 38 |
| 37 |
| 36 |
| 35 |
| 34 |
| 33 |
| 32 |
| 31 |
| 30 |
| 29 |
| 28 |
| 27 |
| 26 |
| 25 |
| 24 |
| 23 |
| 22 |
| 21 |
| 20 |
| 19 |
| 18 |
| 17 |
| 16 |
| 15 |
| 14 |
| 13 |
| 12 |
| 11 |
| 10 |
| 9 |
| 8 |
| 7 |
| 6 |
| 5 |
| 4 |
| 3 |
| 2 |
| 1 |

resolutions

aren't just for the *New Year...*

...you can make them any time. But maybe you can't decide what to do? No sweat! Here's a helping hand.

First, count the number of letters in your first and last names. Add them together, then divide your answer by two. If your answer includes a half, take the next number up (for example, if your answer is five and a half, take six). This is your "resolution number." Here's what to do if your number is six...

Start at the top of the left-hand column below and check off every sixth box. When you get to the bottom of the first column, continue counting at the top of the next. When you get to the bottom of the third column, continue counting at the top of the first. Keep going, checking off every sixth box, skipping any that are checked, until only one unmarked box is left in each column.

Eat more vegetables	Smile more	Help at a charity event
Start a journal	Help a senior	Recycle more
Unclutter my room	Be kinder to my little bro/sis	Take up a new sport
Stop biting my nails	Help more at home	Collect donations for a local charity store
Watch less TV	Be more considerate	Join a club

whatcha gonna do?

top 10

10 things I'd do if I were *invisible*

1
2
3
4
5
6
7
8
9
10

no way!

chart topper

BANDS

GOING UP

GOING DOWN

chart flopper

outrageous!

what do you bring
to your friendship group ?

Do you play a special role? Maybe you do and you don't even realize it.
Take this test and find out! Read the scenarios below, then pick your response – either A, B, C, or D.
Record your answers then turn the page.

1

Your mom has finally agreed to you getting a kitten (or puppy). Which of these do you do first?

A Write a list of everything your new pet will need. Bed, litter box, food... Phew! She needs so much!

B Think of all the fun you can have with your new pet.

C Call your friends to share the news — you're crazy excited!

D Sit down with your mom and talk the whole thing through. This is a big responsibility!

2

Which part of planning a party do you enjoy most?

A Making and sending invitations

B Planning the music

C Planning the games and activities

D Deciding who to invite

3

It's Monday morning and you're ready for school. You have 15 minutes free before you have to leave home. Do you...

A Check your school bag one more time?

B Watch some TV?

C Wait in the car? You're itching to get going!

D Take some time to review your planner for the week?

4

Which of these activities sounds most appealing?

A A room makeover

B Theme-park rides

C A team sport

D Writing stories or poems

organizer

joker

5

What do you find most annoying?

A Messy bedrooms

B Boring movies

C Being on the losing team

D Being rushed into a quick decision

6

You're hanging out with your buds and no one can decide what to do next! Do you...

A Take control and suggest some great ideas?

B Hang back and go along with whatever the group decides?

C Suggest that everyone comes up with an idea, then lead a vote on what to do?

D Help come up with some new ideas by reminding the group of all the great things you've done together?

7

It's the last week of the summer vacation. Which of these would you do first?

A Plan a trip to the mall with your mom to buy all the stuff you'll need for school.

B Throw an end-of-summer sleepover and invite all your friends.

C Get excited about all the great things you'll do in the new school year.

D Create a memory box full of keepsakes from your summer.

8

When traveling with your family, are you most likely to...

A Prepare travel games?

B Lead a sing-along?

C Think of great topics of conversation as you go along?

D Read a book or magazine?

Mostly As, Bs, or Cs? Count 'em up then flip over the page.

what's your score?

what do you bring to your friendship group?

mostly As: THE ORGANIZER

You are a great team player and love to plan group activities, whether it's buying ice cream or arranging a club meeting. Every group needs a friend like you to make sure you make the most of your time together.

mostly Bs: THE JOKER

The Joker is the easy-going member of the group. Despite your label, you're not always cracking jokes, but you are full of fun and rarely get stressed. The Joker is happy to step back and go along with whatever makes her friends happy.

mostly Cs: THE MOTIVATOR

Who gets things going when the group's feeling down? You, that's who! The Motivator always sees the positive side of any situation. While you may not always have a plan, you love to get the group moving and having fun.

mostly Ds: THE THINKER

The Thinker is the quiet member of the group. While you don't like to stand in the spotlight, you're smart and always think before you talk. Your calm and steady attitude helps stop your friends from going totally crazy!

would ya? could ya? *pushing the limits* or playin' safe?

CIRCLE EITHER

(a) So would! (b) Maybe! (c) Never!

THEN TOTAL THE NUMBER OF As, Bs, AND Cs YOU SCORE!

Take a parachute jump	(a)	(b)	(c)
Change your hair color	(a)	(b)	(c)
Snowboard	(a)	(b)	(c)
Chew on a chocolate-coated bug	(a)	(b)	(c)
Go on safari	(a)	(b)	(c)
Star in a reality TV show	(a)	(b)	(c)
Wear your clothes back-to-front for a day	(a)	(b)	(c)
Walk a tightrope	(a)	(b)	(c)
Put your head in a croc's mouth	(a)	(b)	(c)
Sing in front of class	(a)	(b)	(c)
Sleep in a forest	(a)	(b)	(c)
Run a marathon	(a)	(b)	(c)
Take a balloon ride	(a)	(b)	(c)
Tickle a spider	(a)	(b)	(c)
Put your hands in jelly	(a)	(b)	(c)
Ride a camel	(a)	(b)	(c)
Fly to the moon	(a)	(b)	(c)

mostly As

mostly Bs

mostly Cs

would ya? could ya?

mostly As

You have a great attitude! You love to try new things and are first in line for a challenge. You aren't afraid to fail as long as you give it your best shot, and you love being the center of attention. You can be a bit of a show-off, so remember to share the spotlight — it's not always about you!

mostly Bs

Big up! You have a balanced attitude and always think things through before you make a decision. You like to stand back and let your friends try something new before you do, which is cool, but don't be afraid to take the lead from time to time.

mostly Cs

You like to play it safe and will be the first to stop your friends getting into trouble. You are wise, single-minded, and not easily influenced by your friends, but life's an adventure so don't be afraid to try something new once in a while!

YOU

friendship flower

and your best friends

Friendship flowers are a cool way to record the similarities and differences between you and your friends. Make one and discover your friendship connections!

1) Think of two friends.

2) Write your three names in the spaces around the diagram.

3) Write something *unique* about each of you in the light-orange segments.

4) In the mid-orange segments where two circles cross, write something the two people represented by the circles have in common. So if your two friends like ice cream, write "ice cream" in the mid-orange segment where the two circles cross over.

5) Finally, where the three circles cross over in the dark-orange segment, write something the three of you have in common.

6) Try creating friendship flowers for all your friends.

your name..........

your friend's name..........

your friend's name..........

check your

Do you keep your cool while others cringe?

cringe-o-meter

How would you react? Read and rate the following scenarios.

(a)	(b)	(c)	(d)	(e)
This is the worst day of my life.	May the ground swallow me up — now!	It's not good, but I'm keeping calm.	You know what? It could be worse.	What's the problem?
6 points	**4 points**	**2 points**	**1 points**	**0 points**

Your dad crashes your sleepover, dancing the Funky Chicken in his pajamas. (a) (b) (c) (d) (e)

You leave the bathroom with your dress tucked in your underwear! The first to notice is your secret crush. (a) (b) (c) (d) (e)

Your grandma has knitted you a totally unfashionable sweater, and your mom insists you wear it to the mall, where all your friends will see you! (a) (b) (c) (d) (e)

It's time for your solo number in the school musical. You open your mouth to sing and produce the biggest burp — ever. (a) (b) (c) (d) (e)

You experiment with your mom's fake tanning lotion, but mess up. You have streaks all over your face, and they won't wash off. (a) (b) (c) (d) (e)

You've dressed to impress at your BF's party — but two other girls are wearing the same outfit. (a) (b) (c) (d) (e)

You're at a super-cool restaurant with the 'rents and spy a cute boy eyeing you from the next table. When you visit the bathroom, you discover you have pasta sauce all over your face — that's what he's staring at! (a) (b) (c) (d) (e)

Running for the bus you catch your school bag on a gatepost, and fly backwards into a bush. All your buds can see you from the back of the bus! (a) (b) (c) (d) (e)

Your little brother has found a baby picture of you totally naked and shown it to all your friends. (a) (b) (c) (d) (e)

Your mom has a new hairstyle. It looks weird, and worse — she's coming to your school! (a) (b) (c) (d) (e)

mortifying!

As you complete the quiz, shade in one space on the cringe-o-meter for each point you score, starting at the star.

Start here.
Shade in one space
for each point.

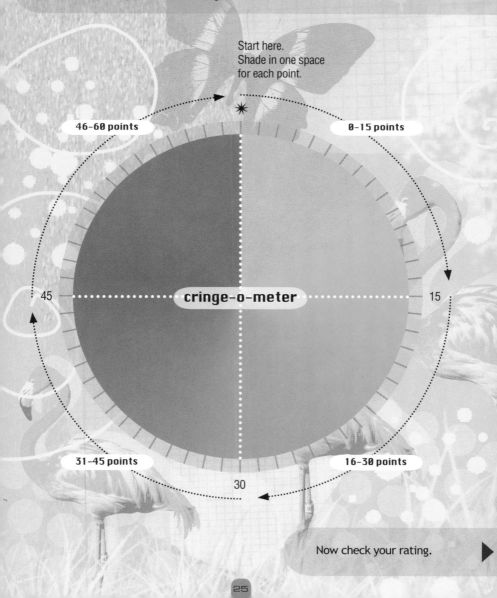

46–60 points

0–15 points

45

cringe-o-meter

15

31–45 points

16–30 points

30

Now check your rating.

check your *cringe-o-meter* results

46–60 points

You know what? Sometimes it might feel like the end of the world, but take a deep breath and count to ten, and you'll view the situation in a whole new light. Take control of mortifying moments by finding the solution, 'fessing up, or seeing the funny side *before* anyone else. And remember that everyone feels consumed by a cringe from time to time!

0–15 points

Does anything phase you? Your level-headed outlook and chilled-out reactions are truly impressive. It's great to be calm, but a very low cringe-o-meter score may suggest that you are too cool to care — and we know that's not true!

31–45 points

You're not comfy in a cringe but manage to keep calm — most of the time. There are times when you wish you could rewind the situation and start again, or just be some place different, but hey, you're only human!

16–30 points

You keep your head together at even the most cringe-worthy moments. You may not be comfortable with the situation, but you know it will pass and don't let it get the better of you.

top 10

10 things I couldn't live *without*

1
2
3
4
5
6
7
8
9
10

must have

my favorite

TV SHOWS

so into it!

GOING UP

GOING DOWN

so over it!

guess what?

zip it!

are you a blabbermouth?

Do you know when to keep it zipped?! Total your As, Bs, and Cs and find out!

1 *Your best friend is crushing on the new boy in school. She's confiding her secret when he walks into the class. Do you...*

Change the subject in a really obvious way, go bright red, and act kind of awkward? (B)

Blurt the news out to her crush? He was going to find out sooner or later. (A)

Pretend you haven't noticed, calmly end your conversation, and take your seat in class? (C)

2 *You overhear your friends planning your surprise birthday party. What do you do?*

Ask if you can join in the prep. (A)

Say nothing and act totally surprised when they throw the party. (C)

Act really cool, but drop big hints about your favorite food, party favors, decorations, etc. (B)

3 *Your mom keeps wearing the bright pink sweater your brother bought her. You know she's just being kind – she thinks it's really horrible! Do you tell him?*

No. He's no fashionista but he scores an A for effort. You say nothing — he'd be mortified if he knew the truth. (C)

No. Don't tell him the truth but make a note to suggest he buys less high-risk gifts next year — chocolates, flowers, that kind of thing.(B)

Yes. She looks like a puffed-up marshmallow! If you don't tell him, he'll keep buying her terrible presents. (A)

4 *You're at the movies with your buds when you remember the latest scoop on the star of the movie! Do you...*

Say nothing until the end of the show? (C)

Tell them as soon as you remember, raising your voice just enough so they can all hear? This news is too hot to hold! (A)

Wait for an appropriate time, then whisper in your neighbor's ear as quietly and quickly as you can? (B)

guess what?

zip it!

5

Your teacher sees you talking in class. Do you...

Keep on talking until your teacher tells you to stop? (A)

Read the signs, finish your sentence, then shut up? (B)

Go red and stop talking at once? (C)

6

You're psyched 'cuz you've bought your mom the most amazing birthday present ever! But her birthday's nearly two months away. Do you...

Store it away and try to forget about it until her birthday comes around? Not easy, but you don't want to spoil the surprise. (C)

Give her the gift early? You just can't resist. (A)

Spend two months dropping hints about the totally cool gift you bought but manage not to give the game away before the big day? (B)

7

You sneaked a peak at your sister's diary. She's graded all her friends, and you, out of 10 and you scored a miserly 3! What do you do?

Feel hurt but take some time to consider why you scored so low — maybe you're not always such a great sister. (C)

Confront her — she may feel bruised about you reading her diary but that's nothing compared with how you feel. (A)

Try to forget it. Let's be honest, you shouldn't have been reading her diary, and there are days when you would score her a zero. (B)

8

You just heard the new girl in school has a totally famous dad! Do you...

Tell everybody? What a scoop! Maybe you'll get to be her friend and hang out with her famous family. (A)

Keep it zipped? It must be a bit weird and embarrassing to have everyone talk about your dad all the time. (C)

Keep it to yourself but tell her you think her dad's really cool? (B)

Mostly As, Bs, or Cs? Count 'em up then flip over the page.

29

what's your score?

are you a blabbermouth?

mostly As

Wow — do you ever stop for breath? You're outgoing and friendly (most of the time) but do you always think before you talk? It's not that you mean to be hurtful, but sometimes telling the whole truth without thinking first can cause a whole lot of trouble. Next time you hear some great gossip, or are just bursting to spill the beans, count to three, and think before you dish!

mostly Bs

You sometimes get the urge to blab, but you also understand that sometimes it's not your place to share the news, however hot off the press! That's not to say you always keep it zipped. You know that sometimes what you hear or discover should be passed on — to the right person at the right time.

mostly Cs

You are sensitive and thoughtful and rarely get the urge to spill the beans. You hate the thought of hurting your friends' feelings or inconveniencing others, and always choose your words carefully. This makes you a great friend to confide in, but remember, sometimes you should share what you hear with a parent or teacher.

pick a pooch

chihuahua

st. bernard

labrador

border collie

greyhound

west highland terrier

Some people say dogs become just like their owners, or is it the other way around? Study this parade of pups, then pick your favorite. What does your pick of the pooches say about YOU?

which **pooch** did you choose?

chihuahua

You're bright, perky, and full of fun. You're outgoing and always try to look on the bright side. You can be a bit of a show-off sometimes but we forgive you because you're sooo adorable!

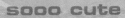 **sooo cute**

st. bernard

You may not be the life of the party and the first to crack a joke, but you are kind, wise, and trustworthy. This means you're probably the first stop when friends need advice or a shoulder to cry on. You have great courage and are a faithful friend.

west highland terrier

You're friendly, fun, and full of energy. You may be small, but you're truly courageous and a loyal friend. Not really one of the crowd, you have inner strength, so you're happy to spend time alone.

i love him

labrador

What a great friend you are! Your kind, gentle, loving personality makes you a devoted lifelong friend. You adjust easily to new places or situations, which makes you the perfect person to help others. Bet you were the first to say "Hi!" to the new girl at school!

border collie

You are hard-working and love to develop your talents and learn new skills. You're not a quitter and will only give up if the game is truly lost. You're always on the look-out for a new adventure and have an infectious sense of fun that makes you a great person to be around.

i want that one

greyhound

Wow! You're full of energy and love outdoor sports and activities. You never seem to get tired and love testing yourself to see just how much you can achieve. Although you're strong and sporty, you have a gentle side and love hanging out with your friends.

top 10

my 10 favorite *celebrities*

1
2
3
4
5
6
7
8
9
10

love him

love her

read it

MAGAZINES

GOING UP

GOING DOWN

leave it

33

are you a worrywart

Do you ever worry that...

- ○ You'll miss the bus?
- ○ You left your bedroom light on?
- ○ When you get to the mall the best clothes will be gone?
- ○ Your dad will act goofy in front of your friends?
- ○ Your armpits smell?
- ○ Your BF will find a new friend?
- ○ You have food stuck in your teeth?
- ○ The boy you're crushing on thinks you're dumb?
- ○ You'll flunk your exams?
- ○ Your mom's dress sense is out of style?
- ○ Your feet are too big?
- ○ You'll be late for school?
- ○ There isn't enough time to get everything done?
- ○ Someone else will eat the last piece of cake?
- ○ Your friends are cooler than you are?

Starting at the left, shade one space if you answer "sometimes," two spaces if you answer "always," and no spaces if you answer "never." At the end of the quiz, check out your smile — is it a cheerful grin or a worrying wobble?

don't worry!

Are you a worrywart?
It's cool and perfectly normal to worry about stuff sometimes— worry can even stop us from doing dumb things, or let us know how much we really care about something or someone. Most worries don't last very long, but if you're worried about something, however stupid it seems, never be afraid to talk to a teacher or a caring adult.

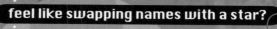

what's your Fame name

Who will you be? You do the math!

Write the first names of TEN stars or celebrities in the first two columns. Then write the LAST names of FIVE stars or celebrities in the third column. (If you like, the names can belong to the stars in the first two columns.)

Count the number of letters in *your* first name, then add it to the number of the season in which you were born (spring = 1, summer = 2, fall = 3, winter = 4). So if your number is eleven...

Start at the top of the left hand column and check off every eleventh box. When you get to the bottom of the first column, continue counting at the top of the next. When you get to the bottom of the third column, continue counting at the top of the first. Keep checking off every eleventh box, skipping any that are checked, until only one unmarked box is left in each column. The last three unmarked boxes contain your fame name!

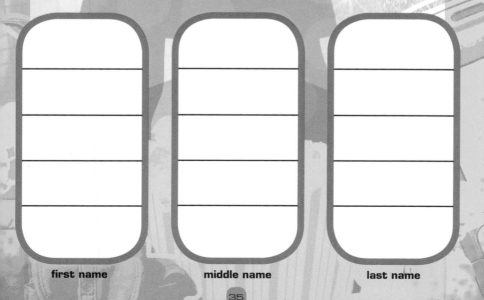

first name   middle name   last name

practice
your

signature

You never know when you might need it!

Rock Star Me

Movie Star Me

Rocket Scientist Me

Royalty Me

Soap Star Me

Famous Author Me

Fashion Designer Me

Just Me

what planet

are you on?

TAKE YOUR PICK FROM A, B, OR C. MAKE A NOTE OF YOUR SCORES, THEN FLIP OVER THE PAGE.

earth dweller

rocket scientist

(a) floaty dress	(b) jeans	(c) overalls
(a) head in the clouds	(b) head in a hat	(c) head in a book
(a) art class	(b) history class	(c) science class
(a) barefoot	(b) boots	(c) sneakers
(a) tie-dye	(b) patterned	(c) plain white
(a) dance-athon	(b) walking in the park	(c) brain training
(a) learning the flute	(b) learning to dance	(c) learning algebra
(a) fruit salad	(b) ice cream	(c) granola
(a) retro tunes	(b) chart hits	(c) classical tracks
(a) bean bag	(b) sofa	(c) office chair
(a) strawberries	(b) chocolate	(c) gum
(a) eclipse of the sun	(b) sunrise	(c) lightning bolt
(a) running late	(b) arriving early	(c) just on time
(a) scrapbooking	(b) bowling	(c) crossword puzzle
(a) performing a mime	(b) performing a song	(c) performing magic

mostly As

mostly Bs

mostly Cs

space cadet

37

outa-space personality

mostly As

SPACE CADET

Your outa-space personality is from another planet. You are creative and not afraid to be different. You love nature, being outdoors, and the simple life. Some people may think you're dancing to a completely different beat, but why not? Just remember to tune in to Planet Earth now and then!

mostly Bs

GROUNDED EARTH DWELLER

You've got your feet on the ground and know how to keep it real 24/7. You love to hang out with like-minded friends and talk about the latest music, fashions, and TV shows. You may not like to stand out in a crowd, but try it once in a while. It's great to develop your own unique qualities.

mostly Cs

ROCKET SCIENTIST

Wow! You are a brainiac in a totally cool way. You love all things scientific and finding out just how far you can strain your brain. You may not always feel that you fit in with your friends, but don't let that hold you back. Without your special skills, there'd never have been a man on the moon!

my secret

celebrity crush ! ! !

Who's the cutest star in Celeb Land? Can't decide? Help is at hand!

(1) Write down your top four celebrity crushes in the first column.

(2) Pick your favorite from the two pairs.

(3) Pick your favorite from the final two. **cute!**

1

2

3

4

cute!

my year

how do you rate it?

at the movies

Movie	JANUARY	Rating
		☺ ☺ ☹
		☺ ☺ ☹
		☺ ☺ ☹
		☺ ☺ ☹

Movie	FEBRUARY	Rating
		☺ ☺ ☹
		☺ ☺ ☹
		☺ ☺ ☹
		☺ ☺ ☹

Movie	MARCH	Rating
		☺ ☺ ☹
		☺ ☺ ☹
		☺ ☺ ☹
		☺ ☺ ☹

Movie	APRIL	Rating
		☺ ☺ ☹
		☺ ☺ ☹
		☺ ☺ ☹
		☺ ☺ ☹

Movie	MAY	Rating
		☺ ☺ ☹
		☺ ☺ ☹
		☺ ☺ ☹
		☺ ☺ ☹

Movie	JUNE	Rating
		☺ ☺ ☹
		☺ ☺ ☹
		☺ ☺ ☹
		☺ ☺ ☹

Every month, record and rate the movies you see at the theater or on TV. Who were your award winners?

Movie	JULY	Rating
		☺ 😐 ☹
		☺ 😐 ☹
		☺ 😐 ☹
		☺ 😐 ☹

Movie	AUGUST	Rating
		☺ 😐 ☹
		☺ 😐 ☹
		☺ 😐 ☹
		☺ 😐 ☹

Movie	SEPTEMBER	Rating
		☺ 😐 ☹
		☺ 😐 ☹
		☺ 😐 ☹
		☺ 😐 ☹

Movie	OCTOBER	Rating
		☺ 😐 ☹
		☺ 😐 ☹
		☺ 😐 ☹
		☺ 😐 ☹

Movie	NOVEMBER	Rating
		☺ 😐 ☹
		☺ 😐 ☹
		☺ 😐 ☹
		☺ 😐 ☹

Movie	DECEMBER	Rating
		☺ 😐 ☹
		☺ 😐 ☹
		☺ 😐 ☹
		☺ 😐 ☹

41

discover your future

fantasy

Take the number of letters in your favorite color and subtract it from your age ten years from now.
This number is the key to your fantasy future! So if your number is twelve...

Start at the top of the left-hand column and check off every twelfth box. When you get to the bottom, start at the top of the next column. When you get to the bottom of the third column, start again at the top of the first column. Keep checking off every twelfth box, skipping any that are already checked, until only one unmarked box is left in each column. What's your result? Sound good?

I'll be a...	Living in...	In a...
Rock Star	U.S.	Penthouse
Movie Star	Britain	Castle
Writer	France	Houseboat
TV Host	Australia	Mansion
Dancer	Hong Kong	Farmhouse

top 10

my 10 best friends ever

1.
2.
3.
4.
5.
6.
7.
8.
9.
10.

forever

triumph

MOVIES

GOING UP

GOING DOWN

turkey

best friend

can you keep your cool ?

Choose from A, B, or C then total your results and turn the page!

1

You suspect the new girl at school is trying to steal your best friend. How do you react?

A If she's new to the school, she's probably feeling kinda scared and lonely. You make an effort to befriend her. Chances are you won't lose your friend, but will gain a new one.

B She is way out of line! How dare she just come here and steal your friend. Drop your so-called friend and put down the new girl every chance you get.

C Oh well, you'll just have to find a new best friend...

2

Your big sis is allowed to stay out late but you have to be home by 7.30pm. What do you do?

A Try some negotiation tactics! For example, ask whether you can stay out later on weekends or during school breaks.

B Deliver an ultimatum. If you can't stay out as late as your sister, you'll refuse to go out at all. Ha! That'll show 'em.

C That's the way it goes. When you're older, you can stay out late. For now, you'll enjoy the extra sleep!

3

Your dad has spilled coffee all over your homework. How do you react?

A Stand back and assess the situation. Can it be saved? If not, you'll have your dad write a note to your teacher explaining his goof-up. (In the future, you'll do your homework far away from the table.)

B Screw it up and burst into tears.

C Keep chilled! When it dries it'll look sort of antique.

4

Your favorite TV show has moved to after 9pm and your parents won't let you stay up. What do you do?

A Ask them to record it for you to watch the next day — easy!

B Get really annoyed and lie in bed unable to sleep knowing your parents (and all your friends, probably) are enjoying YOUR favorite show.

C Skip the show. Hey, it wasn't that great anyway.

5 You suspect someone has been stealing from your locker. What's your plan?

A Make a note of what you leave in the locker, then make sure it's securely locked when you're not around. If things still go missing, you'll talk to your teacher.

B Set a trap, then tackle your suspect when everyone's looking!

C Do nothing. You can replace everything in the locker, so who cares? Maybe the thief needs your stuff more than you do!

6 Your little brother has gotten his own way—again! What do you do?

A Talk to your parents about how you feel. Trouble is, you're so mature, it's easy for them to focus their attention on the baby of the house!

B Refuse to join in any family activities until it's agreed that next time you can have the final say.

C Go with the flow — it's nice to see your kid brother happy.

7 You want to watch your fave show on the big TV, but your dad's watching the game. What do you do?

A Easy. You'll watch the show in your room. It's only fair — after all he did buy the TV.

B You're not going to get your own way but you can be REALLY annoying. You insist on watching the game too but make loud slurpy noises with your drink, crunch on chips, and keep getting up to go to the bathroom.

C You'll miss your show, but who cares? The same thing happens every week anyway!

8 You can't sleep because your big brother is playing his music too loud. How do you react?

A It's radical, but sometimes being nice to him works. Explain that you're really tired and ask nicely if he'll turn the music down. If not, draft in the 'rents to lay down the law.

B Play your music loud too! OK, you're not going to get any sleep, but at least you're drowning out your brother's grungy tunes.

C Put a pillow over your ears and count sheep.

Mostly As, Bs or Cs? Count 'em up then flip over the page.

what's your score ?

can you keep your cool?

mostly As

Congratulations! It's not always easy but most of the time you manage to keep your cool. You know when to stand up and when to back off, and most of the time manage to catch a deep breath before you jump in.

mostly Bs

Hmmm! You have a clear sense of right and wrong but don't always go about things the right way. Sometimes being sensible is just too dry — you like to mix it up with some major confrontations. This may occasionally get results but, as you know, you get the *best* results when you keep calm and stay in control.

mostly Cs

You certainly keep cool, but maybe you're a bit too relaxed. You might give the impression that you're so laid back you just don't care. Don't be afraid of being assertive when it comes to something you really believe in. It's natural to get hot and bothered once in a while!

pick a shoe

ballet shoes

sneakers

cozy slippers

rain boots

dress shoes

beach sandals

Do your style choices reveal the real you? Take a long look at the shoes, make your choice and then flip over the page!

which shoe did you choose?

ballet shoes

You have a creative, artistic personality and love all things pretty and pink. You're organized and hate mess! You dream of being on the stage and would love to be a dancer.

so beautiful

sneakers

You're always on the move and love sports, dancing, or anything that keeps your feet moving. You love hanging out with your friends and taking part in group activities.

cozy slippers

You are a total homebody and love staying in with your buds and family. You're a warm and happy personality who's always there for her friends. Awww!

i love these

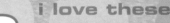

rain boots

You love to be outside come rain or shine! You love nature and have a great sense of adventure. You can be a bit of a tomboy and don't care if you get wet or muddy!

dress shoes

You dress to impress. You are a perfectionist and your snappy style always gets you noticed. You are ambitious and ready to work hard to achieve your goals. You go, girl!

stunning

beach sandals

You're a hippy chic who dreams of desert islands and lazy days! You love to be outdoors in the sunshine. Your perfect vacation would be spent swimming with dolphins and searching for seashells!

top 10

my favorite restaurant *food*

1.
2.
3.
4.
5.
6.
7.
8.
9.
10.

delicious

tasty

gotta see it!

SOAPS

GOING UP

GOING DOWN

give it a miss!

is fame in your future?

are you a star?

How far will you walk along the RED CARPET? Every time you answer YES to one of the questions below, shade a footprint on the red carpet. Start at the bottom.

Will you make it to HOLLYWOOD?

- Do you ever put on shows for your friends and family?
- Would you audition for a TV talent show?
- Have you ever been the lead in a school play?
- Do you like having your picture taken?
- Have you ever sung in front of your parents?
- Are you competitive?
- Do you dress to be different?
- Have you ever taken dance classes?
- Do you like to be the center of attention at parties?
- Do you have a good memory?
- Do you believe practice makes perfect?
- Would you rather be well known than well paid?
- Do you know the words to your favorite song?
- Do you think famous people are "just like you and me?"
- Do you ever practice writing your autograph?
- Do you enjoy working hard?
- Does praise make you feel great?
- Do you love to learn new skills?
- Do you like to make your friends laugh?
- Are you patient?

16 - 20
Born to be a star!

6 - 15
You've got what it takes so who knows?

up to 5
Happy to shine on the inside

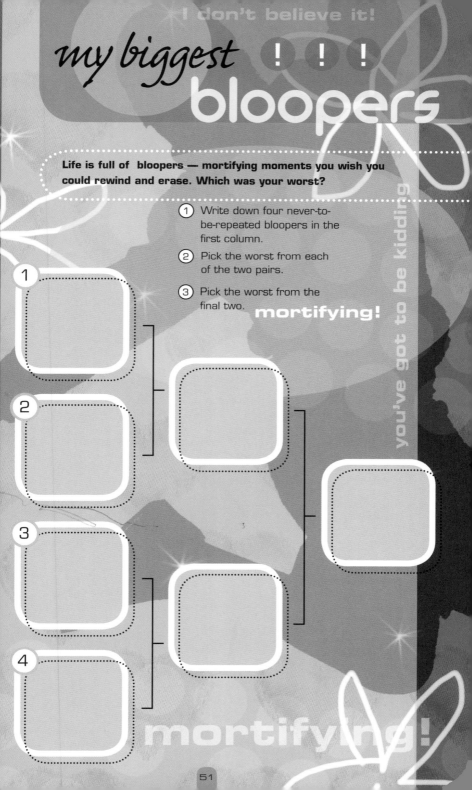

my biggest !!! bloopers

Life is full of bloopers — mortifying moments you wish you could rewind and erase. Which was your worst?

(1) Write down four never-to-be-repeated bloopers in the first column.

(2) Pick the worst from each of the two pairs.

(3) Pick the worst from the final two.

mortifying!

you've got to be kidding

1

2

3

4

mortifying!

are you a
diva?

Pick your answer a, b, c, or d, then total your scores!
Flip over the page to find out how Diva-ish you are!

1

You're finally allowed a pet. Awesome! Which will you choose?

A A cute kitten with big sad eyes. You can't wait to give her a safe, warm home.(1)

B A pocket-sized pooch you can carry in your bag. After all, dogs are a fashion accessory, aren't they? (6)

C A goldfish. They don't need exercise, don't eat too much, and won't poop on the carpet! (2)

D A virtual pet. It's not real but it doesn't eat, so it's the ultimate in low-cost pets! (3)

2

You are in a long line at the fashion store and just know that you're going to be late for the movie. Do you...

A Push to the front of the line and insist on being served immediately? Don't they know who you are? People can be sooo selfish. (6)

B Come back another day when the store is less busy? It's more important to meet your friends and have fun. (2)

C Politely ask the people in front of you if they'd mind you being served first? They'll probably say "no," but it's surprising what you can achieve if you ask nicely. (1)

D Stay in line even though you'll be late for your buds? Friends are for life but fashion is forever! (4)

3

There is one chocolate-chip cookie left in the jar. Do you...

A Eat it but bake some more as a surprise for your mom? (1)

B Take it but buy some more cookies when you're passing the store on your way home from school? (2)

C Eat it? No question! You're hungry, it's yours. Period! (6)

D Leave it in the jar? You've probably had your fair share already! (0)

4

As a birthday treat for your little brother, your mom has planned a family day at the petting zoo. Do you...

A Absolutely refuse to go? You're way to cool to pet animals with your little brother. (6)

B Explain that you feel too old for the zoo and suggest an alternative, for example, a meal for the whole family at a local restaurant? (2)

C Go to the zoo and have a blast? The animals are cute and it's great to have a day out as a family. (1)

D Go along with the zoo plan? It's lame but when it's your turn to pick a treat, you'll take your revenge! (4)

kinda shy

all about me

---

(5)

The school drama club is holding auditions for "Grease!" Do you...

A Sign up straight away? Work hard and your dream of being Sandy may come true. (3)

B Accept there are better singers in your class but go for the auditions anyway? If your singing doesn't make the grade, helping behind the scenes will be great! (2)

C Totally expect to be cast as Sandy and refuse to audition? Haven't they heard your fabulous voice? (6)

D Pass on the auditions? You're kinda shy and the thought of getting up on stage with all your friends watching makes you freak. (1)

---

(6)

You're having a massive argument with your mom over something stupid and have just realized that she's right! Oops! What do you do?

A Carry on arguing. There's still a chance that your mom'll back down. Winning an argument is way more important than being right! (6)

B Change the subject fast. Argument? Who was arguing? Not you! (4)

C Admit defeat. You feel kinda stupid but your mom was right. (1)

D Carry on arguing, go silent for a while, then fess up later when it doesn't seem so important. (3)

---

(7)

Your best friend's sleepover is tonight but your mom says you can't go unless you tidy your room first! Do you...

A Cancel all plans so you can have your room neat and tidy in time for the sleepover? It's a drag but your room IS a mess, so it's a fair trade. (1)

B Produce a list of all the things you have to do and demand to know how, with your schedule totally maxed-out, you are expected to find time to tidy your room? (6)

C Quickly pack everything under your bed, in your dresser, or wherever? Hopefully your efforts will make the grade! (3)

D Offer a compromise? Suggest that you clean some of your room today, go to the sleepover, and then finish up tomorrow when you have more time. (2)

Flip over the page to find out how Diva-ish you are!

53

what's your score ?

are you a diva?

33–42 points

Move outta the way, Ms. D is in town! You are a strong character and know exactly what you want! You ooze confidence and truly love yourself! Think, though — are you so into yourself that you sometimes overlook your family and friends? Letting your "Diva self" out and being the center of attention once in a while can be fun but not many people can live with a Diva 24/7.

26–32 points

You have your Diva moments. You're single-minded and like to be center stage once in a while. However, you are considerate of other people's feelings, and while you like to have your own way, you know when to compromise. You like the finer things in life and are happy to work hard to get them.

6–25 points

You're as sweet as grandma's apple pie and tend to think of other people before yourself. You may not feel comfortable in the spotlight but don't be afraid to take center stage once in a while. Take time out for some "me-time" and think about what you'd like to achieve. It's great that you put others first, but think about what you want too.

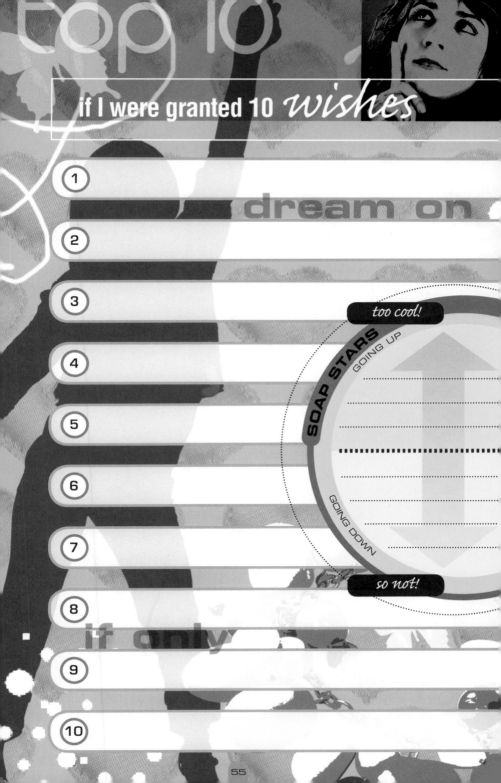

top 10

if I were granted 10 *wishes*

dream on

1

2

3

4

5

6

7

8

9

10

too cool!

SOAP STARS

GOING UP

GOING DOWN

so not!

if only

which chocolate center are you?

Are you a Strawberry cream, a Hard caramel, or a totally Nutty cluster? Follow the flow and find out.

gold
silver

puppies
panthers

bubble bath
shower

surfing the net
surfing the waves

happy to wait
want it now!

writing a story
reading a book

play to win
play for fun

riding horses
fun fair

so serious
so funny

work
play

soap
reality show

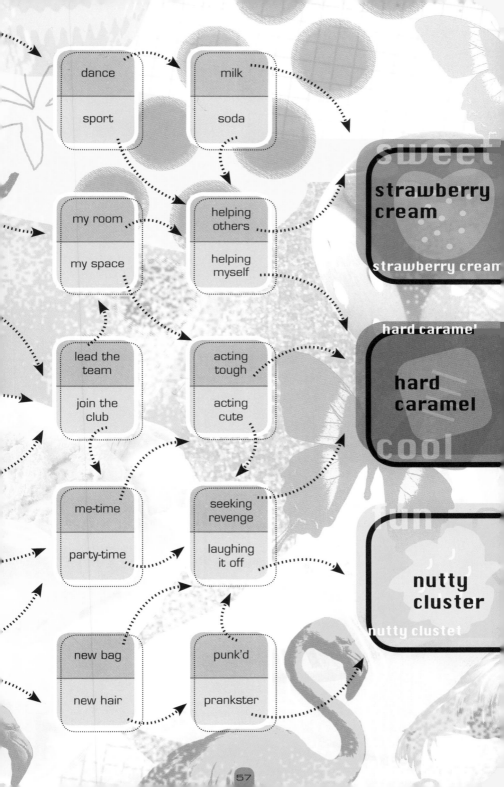

dance
sport

milk
soda

my room
my space

helping others
helping myself

sweet

strawberry cream

strawberry cream

lead the team
join the club

acting tough
acting cute

hard caramel

hard caramel

cool

me-time
party-time

seeking revenge
laughing it off

fun

nutty cluster

nutty cluster

new bag
new hair

punk'd
prankster

57

results

which chocolate center are you?

sweet

strawberry cream

strawberry cream

You really are as sweet as candy. Strawberry creams are kind and caring and try to have a good word for everybody. They will be the first to cheer a friend who's down, or offer a helping hand to a friend in a fix. Your heart is kind, but don't forget to think of yourself sometimes, Strawberry cream!

hard caramel

hard caramel

cool

Deep inside you're sugary sweet but you are strong, courageous, and a faithful friend. You are not afraid to stand up for what you believe in, even if it means you someimes upset your friends. It's cool to be caramel, just don't be afraid to show your sweet side from time to time!

fun

nutty cluster

nutty cluster

Nutty clusters are always up for fun, parties, and jokes. They make great friends 'cuz there's never a dry moment when a Nutty cluster's around! It's great to be the life of the party, but don't forget to show your serious side once in a while too.

top 10

10 stops on my *world tour*

Where in the world would you go?

1.
2.
3.
4.
5.
6.
7.
8.
9.
10.

interesting

exciting

totally dreamy

GOING UP

BIRTHDAY SURPRISES

GOING DOWN

worst nightmare

laugh or cry ?

Sometimes life just doesn't go your way! Assess each situation. Would you...

a) see the funny side?

b) be mortified?

Each time you answer b), randomly shade in one of the "teeth" black. Will you have a gleaming, happy-go-lucky smile or a gap-tooth grimace?

○ You got the recipe wrong and the cake you baked is totally unappetizing.

○ Your mom catches you singing in the shower.

○ Your secret crush traces his Valentine's card back to you.

○ Your friend points out you've been walking around with toilet paper stuck to your shoe.

○ You leave your secret diary out and catch your sis reading it!

○ You dad uses his nickname for you (and it's totally embarrassing, something like "cookie crumb") in front of your friends!

○ You sneeze and fire a booger onto your math teacher's blouse.

○ You're at a posh restaurant and drink so much soda you get uncontrollable burps!

○ Your brother lets off a stink bomb and blames you. Everyone believes him!

○ You're showing off some new dance moves and slip, landing on your rear!

keep smilin'

my favorite ! ! !
teacher

Which teacher brings out the best in you?
Can't decide? Here's some help!

1. Write the names of your four favorite teachers in the first column.

2. Pick your favorite from the two pairs.

3. Pick your favorite from the final two.

Grade A result!

I know the answer!

1

2

3

4

Grade A result!

are you a control freak ?

Choose from A, B, or C, then total your results and turn the page!

1 Before leaving home for an afternoon at the mall, which of these is most important?

A Making a list of all the stuff you need to buy.

B Checking how much money you have.

C Visiting the bathroom.

2 You've invited your friends for a sleepover. Do you . . .

A Plan the evening up front, from music and food to what to wear and how to fix your hair?

B Have your friends bring their fave music, food, and games? It'll be great to mix things up!

C Do nothing? It's cool to be totally chilled and let the party just happen!

3 The most annoying thing about your little brother (or friend's brother) is...

A He won't do what you say.

B He acts like a little kid.

C Nothing really, he's OK.

4 You join the school Journalism club. Which job has YOUR name on it?

A Editor.

B Reporter.

C None — you're happy not to have a specific job, but will help out wherever you're needed.

5 You're asked to help produce the end of the year play. Is this...

A The perfect use of your organizational skills?

B A great opportunity to have fun with your friends after school?

C Your worst nightmare?

6 Have a look in your bag. What do you see?

A Everything you could possibly need through the day.
B Money, keys, a pen — just the usual stuff.
C Things you forgot you had!

7 Do you keep your books/DVDs/CDs/games on shelves in alphabetical order?

A Of course!
B I try, but they get a bit mixed up.
C You're kidding, right?

8 Your BF throws you a surprise birthday party. How do you react?

A Total freak-out! You hate surprises.
B Feel really touched that your friends care so much.
C A bit shocked. You don't really like all the attention, but you're happy to go with the flow.

9 The best thing about sports is...

A Leading a team to victory.
B Having fun with your buddies.
C Nothing — all sports stink!

10 Which is worse?

A Losing an argument.
B Losing your lunch money.
C Losing your place in a book.

Mostly As, Bs, or Cs? Count 'em up then flip over the page.

what's your score ?

are you a control freak?

mostly As

You love to be in control and are not afraid to make decisions! These are great qualities, but watch you don't get grumpy if things don't go your way! Being assertive and taking charge is fine — hey, one day you may become a world leader — but take time out to relax and let someone else run the show once in a while.

mostly Bs

You're no control freak but that doesn't mean you don't like to have things go your way now and again. The thought of taking charge may make you feel a bit nervous, but your relaxed nature means you can really get the best from people. Have a try — chances are you'll be surprised by the results.

mostly Cs

You're easy going and happy to let others take charge. But beware — sometimes you're so relaxed, people might get the impression that you don't care — and we know that's not true! Try stepping up to the plate once in a while; you might be surprised by how rewarding it is.

top 10

favorite *names* 5 boys and 5 girls

1

love it

2

3

treasure it!

4

5

IN MY WARDROBE

GOING UP

6

GOING DOWN

7

trash it!

8

cute

9

10

you

and the stars!

friendship flower

What have you got in common with your favorite music stars? Discover your celebrity connections!

1) Think of your two favorite music stars.

2) Write your name plus theirs in the spaces around the diagram.

3) Write something *unique* about each of you in the light-pink segments.

4) In the mid-pink segments, where the circles cross, write something that the two people represented have in common.

5) Finally, in the central, dark segment, write something all three of you have in common. It can be anything you like — maybe you have the same color hair, live at home with your parents, or have travelled to the same places.

6) Try creating celebrity friendship flowers for all your favorite stars and see what you have in common!

your name

singer's name

singer's name

where will you live?

town or country

Are you a natural country dweller, or were you born to be high-rise in the city? Take your pick from A or B. Then, starting at the bottom, shade in yellow the number of windows given by each answer. How many lights will you turn on?

(a) fresh milk **(0 windows)**	(b) soda **(2 windows)** ✓
(a) out late **(2)** ✓	(b) up early **(1)**
(a) taxi ride **(2)**	(b) pony ride **(0)** ✓
(a) mud **(0)**	(b) concrete **(2)**
(a) restaurant **(2)**	(b) picnic **(1)** ✓
(a) goldfish **(2)**	(b) puppy **(1)**
(a) fruit pie **(1)**	(b) hot dog **(2)**
(a) disco **(2)**	(b) barn dance **(0)**
(a) air conditioning **(2)**	(b) fresh air **(1)**
(a) rain boots **(0)**	(b) heels **(2)**
(a) vegetable patch **(0)**	(b) mall **(2)**
(a) riding a bike **(1)**	(b) riding a bus **(2)**
(a) old friends **(1)**	(b) new friends **(2)**
(a) bright light **(2)**	(b) starlight **(0)**
(a) noisy streets **(2)**	(b) quiet lanes **(0)**

19 - 30

Sitting pretty in the city

13 - 18

Town or country, home is where your heart is!

up to 12

Country comforts

30
29
28
27
26
25
24
23
22
21
20
19
18
17
16
15
14
13
12
11
10
9
8
7
6
5
4
3
2
1

my ultimate !!! snack

Potato chips or breadsticks, marshmallows or muffins, popcorn or pecans. What's your ultimate SNACK?

1. Write down your four favorite snacks — two sweet and two salty in the first column.
2. Pick your favorite from the two pairs.
3. Pick the best from the final two. **feelin' hungry?**

1

2

3

4

just sooo delicious!

feelin' hungry?

pick a hat

beret

wool hat

baseball cap

01

straw hat

tiara

space helmet

Can your hat reveal you inner personality? Do you wear your heart on your HEAD?! Take a look at the hats on this page, then pick your favorite — turn the page to discover what your choice says about you!

which hat did you choose?

beret

Sassy and stylish, the beret is the hat of choice for artists and girls who aim to be a little bit different. Berets, whether plain or in a funky pattern, are confident, fun-loving, and truly individual.

looks good

wool hat

A cute wool hat is a sign of a warm and kind personality. You may put comfort before style, sometimes but hey, who cares? Your honest, open nature makes you a special friend and confidante.

baseball cap

You are independent, sporty, and a great team player. You love the outdoors and are fun to hang out with. You also love to win and are not afraid to show your competitive side!

i love this one

straw hat

You are fun, floaty, and a romantic at heart! You love sunny days, picnics on the beech, and chillin' with your buds! Your happy, sunny, personality means you're always fun to be around.

crown

You love the finer things in life and dream of being carried away by Prince Charming on his white stallion! You have a regal style that makes you the center of attention wherever you go!

suits me

space helmet

You have the spirit of an explorer and would love to fly to the moon! You have a thirst for knowledge and love traveling to new and exciting places.

top 10

Who would win your
entertainment awards?

Best Actor goes to

Best Actress goes to

Best Recording Artist (male) goes to

Best Recording Artist (female) goes to

Best Group goes to

Best Song goes to

Best Film goes to

Best TV Show goes to

Best Play goes to

Best Author goes to

what
kind of
Friend
are
you?

Quiet and thoughtful, full of ideas, or a shoulder to cry on?

Check off your **eight** favorite activities and count up how many of each color you have chosen. Then flip over the page — do your choices reveal the real you?

sleepovers

going to the theater/ movies

ice skating

reading a book

playing musical instruments

horse/pony riding

shopping

acting

crafts

dancing

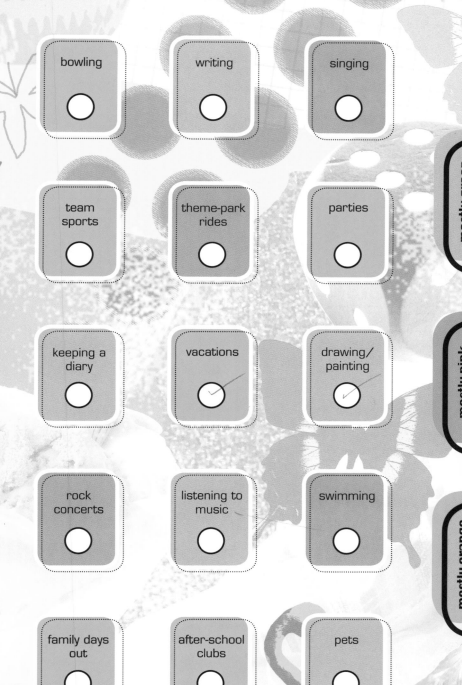

bowling

writing

singing

team sports

theme-park rides

parties

keeping a diary

vacations

drawing/ painting

rock concerts

listening to music

swimming

family days out

after-school clubs

pets

mostly green

mostly pink

mostly orange

73

results

what kind of friend are you?

busy

mostly green

You are thoughtful, creative, and happy to spend time alone. You don't like being the center of attention, but your thoughtful nature means you're a great listener and the first stop when your friends have problems or want to enjoy some quiet time.

energy

mostly pink

You are full of energy and love to get out and enjoy life to the full. You love hanging out with your buds and are happy to have lots of friends rather than stick to one group. You're full of great ideas and a fun friend to have around.

sweet

mostly orange

You're a real team player and love being part of a group. You are outgoing and tend to stick to one group of friends. You're loyal and will be the first on the scene if your friends are in trouble or need a helping hand.

top 10

my *heroes*

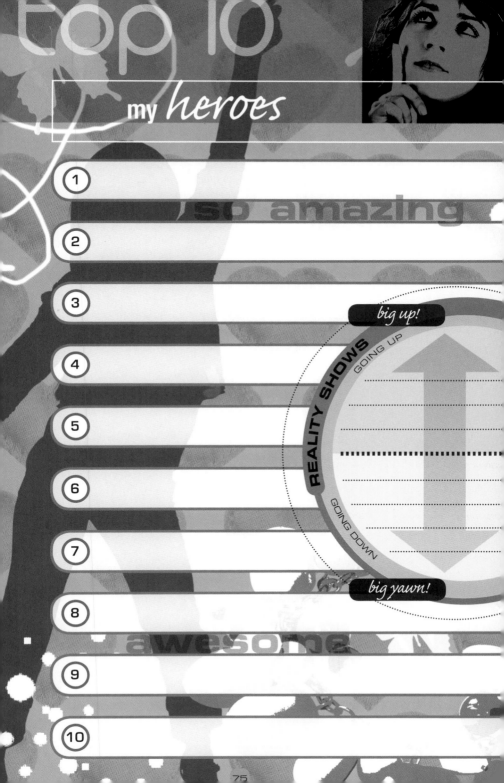

1
2
3

so amazing

big up!

REALITY SHOWS

GOING UP

GOING DOWN

4
5
6
7

big yawn!

awesome

8
9
10

stand out

fit in

are you

one of a kind or one of the crowd?

Unique or united? Take the test, tally your score, then turn the page!

1

Your BFs have had their hair cut in cute bobs. Suddenly your 'do feels so last year! Do you...

1 Style your hair in a bob just like your friends'? It looks sooo cool! (4)

2 Keep your hair as it is? It's out of style but you haven't got time to pick a new 'do! (3)

3 Flip through some celeb magazines to find a new look? Anything but a bob! (2)

4 Have your stylist suggest some new styles that will suit your face? (1)

2

If you could sit anywhere in class, would you...

1 Sit by the teacher? (0)

2 Sit with your BFF? (2)

3 Sit with the brainiacs? You might need some help! (1)

4 Sit with the most popular class members? (4)

3

Your friends are heading for the school play auditions. You'd love to try out but it's a musical and you're totally tone deaf! Do you...

1 Skip the auditions and find something you can excel at? (1)

2 Watch the auditions from the back of the hall and wish you had a cool voice just like your friends? (3)

3 Try out anyway and cringe as they ROTFL? (4)

4 Find out if there are any nonsinging roles or opportunities backstage? (2)

4

All your friends are drinking coffee but you'd rather have juice. Do you...

1 Pour yourself a juice? (0)

2 Take the coffee but ditch it in a planter when no one is looking? (3)

3 Sip up the coffee? Ugh! (4)

4 Say you're not thirsty? (2)

76

5

Your BFs held a yard sale and bought adorable cropped denim jackets with the proceeds. Do you…

1 Beg your 'rents for the cash to buy a jacket just like your friends'? (4)

2 Admire the jacket and wonder if it would suit you? (2)

3 Come up with a cash-generating scheme of your own so you can afford one too? (3)

4 Cross the jacket off your wish list? Now that your buds have one, it's just not special. (0)

6

Do you love reading about celebrities?

1 Yes! Me and my buds love to laugh at their fashion goof-ups. (3)

2 No, because their lives seem so unreal. (2)

3 Yes, because I'd love to be famous too someday. (4)

4 No, because sometimes what the magazines say seems so cruel. (0)

7

Your friends are sending each other text messages in class. You know it's against the rules. Do you…

1 Do nothing? You always turn your cell off before class. (0)

2 Just read the messages but don't reply? You can't afford to miss out on the latest gossip! (2)

3 Join in? It's only math after all. (4)

4 Send a couple of messages but feel really bad and hope your teacher doesn't notice. (3)

8

Your friends are hooked on new soap, "Heathcliffe High," but you'd rather watch the nature show on the other channel. Do you…

1 Record the soap so you can watch it before school the next day? It's a drag but it'll mean you can join in the conversation. (3)

2 Miss your show and watch the soap? Who cares — nature is sooo dull! (4)

3 Skip the soap and try to change the subject when your buds begin to discuss it? (2)

4 Don't watch the soap and hang back when it's discussed at school the next day? (0)

Total your scores and turn the page!

77

what's your score ?

are you one of a kind or one of the crowd?

0–11 points

Wow! You truly have your own style! You love who you are and your difference makes you a stand-out member of your group. Being unique is cool, as long as when you disagree, you are expressing your true feelings, not just making a statement to look different. It's OK to like the same things as your friends sometimes — that's one of the reasons you get along!

12–25 points

You enjoy hanging out with your friends and are happy to go with the flow on occasion, but remain a true individual who isn't afraid to stand up for something she believes in. Your individuality only makes your friends love you more!

26–32 points

You love to be part of the group. You feel most comfortable with like-minded friends, and you are happy to sacrifice some of your individuality to fit in. It's understandable that you want to be just like your friends but don't be afraid to develop your own style. Break out once in a while and show the world the real you!

top 10

my 10 *firsts*

My first **school**

remember?

My first **BFF**

My first **CD**

My first **movie**

My first **party**

My first **crush**

the best!

My first **pet**

My first **vacation**

My first **teacher**

My first **award**
(If you haven't won anything yet, don't worry, you've got plenty of time!)

do your friend

Who knows you best? Write your friends' names at the top of each column, then check a box each time they get a question correct. Total their scores at the bottom.

What's my favorite color?

What's my favorite TV show?

What's my middle name?

Who's my secret crush?

How old was I on my last birthday?

What's my address?

Close your eyes. What color are my eyes?

How do you spell my last name?

What's my favorite class?

What's my favorite ice-cream flavor?

How many brothers/sisters do I have?

Who's my favorite recording artist?

Who's my favorite author?

What's my mom's name?

What's my favorite candy bar?

name	Aubrie											
	✓											
	✓											
	✓											
	✓											
	✓											
	✓											
	✓											
	✓											
	✓											
	✓											
	✓											
total												

which show do you love

TV week

List every TV show you watch for a week and circle or check one of the ratings. How was your week's viewing? Time well spent or a total turn off?

MONDAY

TV show	Rating
	☺ ☐ ☹
	☺ ☐ ☹
	☺ ☐ ☹
	☺ ☐ ☹
	☺ ☐ ☹
	☺ ☐ ☹

TUESDAY

TV show	Rating
	☺ ☐ ☹
	☺ ☐ ☹
	☺ ☐ ☹
	☺ ☐ ☹
	☺ ☐ ☹
	☺ ☐ ☹

WEDNESDAY

TV show	Rating
	☺ ☐ ☹
	☺ ☐ ☹
	☺ ☐ ☹
	☺ ☐ ☹
	☺ ☐ ☹
	☺ ☐ ☹

THURSDAY

TV show	Rating
	☺ ☺ ☹
	☺ ☺ ☹
	☺ ☺ ☹
	☺ ☺ ☹
	☺ ☺ ☹
	☺ ☺ ☹

FRIDAY

TV show	Rating
	☺ ☺ ☹
	☺ ☺ ☹
	☺ ☺ ☹
	☺ ☺ ☹
	☺ ☺ ☹
	☺ ☺ ☹

SATURDAY

TV show	Rating
	☺ ☺ ☹
	☺ ☺ ☹
	☺ ☺ ☹
	☺ ☺ ☹
	☺ ☺ ☹
	☺ ☺ ☹

SUNDAY

TV show	Rating
	☺ ☺ ☹
	☺ ☺ ☹
	☺ ☺ ☹
	☺ ☺ ☹
	☺ ☺ ☹
	☺ ☺ ☹

my biggest ! ! !
Fashion *disaster*

Everyone loves to try a new trend, but sometimes the results are more uber-cringe than uber-cool! Follow the flow to identify your most traumatic fashion fiasco.

(1) In the first column, write down four dud looks you'll never rerun.

(2) Pick the worst from the two pairs.

(3) Pick the worst from the final two. **shameful!**

1

2

3

4

shameful!

top 10

favorite *love songs*

1.
2.
3.
4.
5.
6.
7.
8.
9.
10.

romantic

VEGETABLES

yum!

GOING UP

GOING DOWN

yuck!

sing along

how do you cope in a crisis ?

freaked out

super cool

Check out the scenarios then pick an answer and total your scores!

1

It's the day before your birthday and you've just had the worst 'do of your life! Do you...

A Try to make it better with a last-minute home cut?
Yikes! It's even worse! (1)

B Sleep on it (literally!) then decide it looks kinda out-there cool? (5)

C Rock the look with a big hat? *So* this season! (4)

D Borrow your grandma's wig? (2)

2

You've left your cell on the bus. Do you...

A Burst into tears and vow never to have another cell because they're too much trouble? (1)

B Call the bus company and ask if anyone has handed in your cell? (3)

C Dial the cell and see if anyone answers it?
If they do, you can ask them to return it to your school. (4)

D Do nothing? Hey, it's a great excuse to buy a new cell! (5)

3

Your end of the year assignment is due tomorrow and you totally forgot! Do you...

A Try writing it super-fast and end up throwing it away?
It's a real stinker! (1)

B Cancel your plans for the evening and focus on getting the assignment done? It should only take a couple of hours. (4)

C 'Fess up to your diary disaster and ask your teacher for more time? (3)

D Play sick? It'll give you a couple of days to write your assignment. (5)

4

Your little brother read your diary and has the scoop on your secret crush! Do you...

A Do nothing? Who cares? If your crush finds out maybe he'll ask you on a date. (5)

B Never forgive him? He's the worst brother ever! (1)

C Politely point out that your diary is none of his business and stow it away in a safer place? (4)

D Beg him not to tell anyone what he read? You'd be totally mortified! (2)

86

(5)

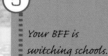
Your BFF is switching schools. Do you...

A Find a new BFF and forget about the old one in a couple of weeks? (5)

B Ditch her? If she were a true friend, she wouldn't move! (1)

C Become really upset? You can't see how you'll ever find such a good friend again! (3)

D Think it'll be a great chance to meet new people and share her new experiences? (4)

(6)

You're messin' with your BFs and accidentally break your mom's favorite vase! Do you...

A Have a total conniption fit and try to mend it with glue and tape? (2)

B Carefully collect all the broken pieces and put them in a safe place for when you 'fess up later? (3)

C Hope she doesn't notice? It's a rotten old vase anyway. (5)

D Burst into tears and tell your friends to go home? Who can have fun after such a major catastrophe? (1)

(7)

It's the day before your BF's birthday and you forgot to buy her gift! Do you...

A Bake cookies and wrap them up in a pretty box? A personal touch, and sooo cute! (3)

B Rush out to your local gift store and buy the first thing you see? Anything's better than nothing! (1)

C Forget the gift and sing her a song or perform a special birthday dance the next time you see her? That will be way better than a store-bought gift and original too. (5)

D Stay cool? You have a special supply of gifts in your closet. (4)

(8)

You're playing lead in the school show but have totally lost your voice! Do you...

A Suggest you could mime your part, or maybe hold up cards with the words on? (3)

B Volunteer to help backstage and let your understudy enjoy being the star of the show? (5)

C Insist the show is cancelled, or at the very least re-written so you don't have to say anything? (2)

D Vow never to be in another show? It's not worth it, it's not fair and the show was a total dud anyway. (1)

Turn over to discover how you cope in a crisis!

what's your score ❓

how do you cope in a crisis?

8–20 points

Eeek — major panic! Sometimes you care so much that when things go wrong, you think it's a total disaster. Take a deep breath and look at the situation again. See, things aren't so bad after all!

21–30 points

Hey, check you out, Ms. Calm and Collected! You seem to have the balance just right. Nobody's perfect, but you care that things go right and generally think of smart solutions when things go wrong.

31–40 points

Hmmm, you certainly keep cool, but maybe you can be a little too relaxed. It's great not to panic, but it may look as though you don't really care, and we know that's not true!

test your patience

ARE YOU HAPPY TO WAIT YOUR TURN, OR DO YOU WANT IT ALL NOW? SCORE ONE POINT EACH TIME YOU AGREE WITH THE STATEMENTS BELOW, THEN TURN THE PAGE TO FIND OUT HOW PATIENT YOU ARE.

I wish I could have more than one birthday a year. ○

I'd love a puppy but training her would be sooo boring. ○

I prefer to learn a game as I go along rather than read the instructions first. ○

Hair extensions are great 'cuz you don't have to wait for your hair to grow. ○

If I see a word I can't read, I skip it. ○

I'm happy to do lots of things at once. ○

I prefer TV shows to movies. ○

If I'm reading a book, I sometimes sneak a peek at the last page to see what happens at the end. ○

If there's a long line in a store, it's best to leave and come back later. ○

I wish my handwriting were neat. ○

If at first you don't succeed, give up! ○

I dream of becoming an overnight sensation. ○

I can't wait until I'm older. ○

It's really annoying when birthday gifts are too tightly wrapped. ○

I'd love to learn a musical instrument, but I think I'd get bored after a few lessons. ○

I can't wait until I have my own place. ○

My friends take sooo long to get ready to go out! ○

I would always take a ride rather than walk. ○

Sometimes I can't sleep because I'm so excited about the next day. ○

hurry up and turn the page ▶

I can't wait

want it now?

0-5 points

You're laid back and happy to wait your turn, letting things happen in their own good time. You have a grounded view of what you can achieve and how you can realize your goals. Your level-headed outlook is cool, but a little impatience can be a sign of ambition and enthusiasm — so don't always fight it!

6-15 points

You have the perfect combination of patience and enthusiasm to get going and get things done. You know you can't have everything you want just when you want it, but that doesn't stop you from dreaming and planning. You understand that often the journey is just as exciting and rewarding as the destination!

16-20 points

Slow down — you're in danger of wishing your life away. It's great to be enthusiastic and super-keen to get great results, but sometimes it's the slow burner who takes the prize (remember the tale of *The Hare and the Tortoise*?) It's frustrating when things don't work out the way you want right away, but accomplishments often feel all the more special when you've had to go the extra mile to achieve them.

top 10

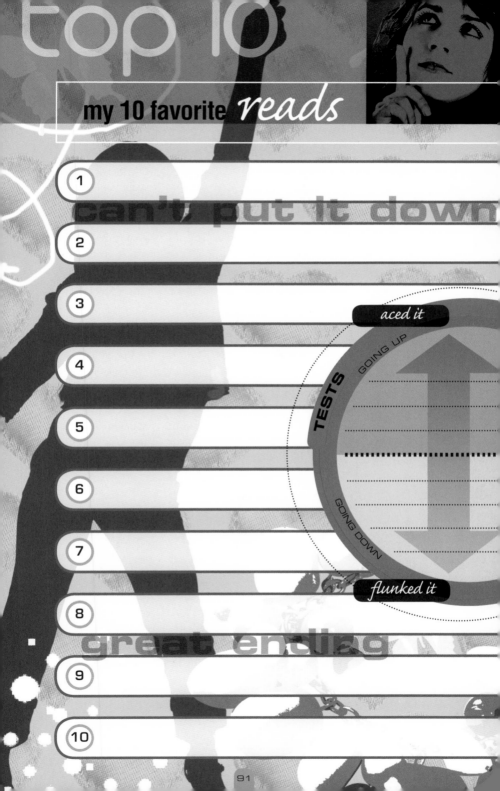

my 10 favorite *reads*

1

can't put it down

2

3

aced it

4

TESTS

GOING UP

5

6

GOING DOWN

7

flunked it

8

great ending

9

10

YOU

and your favorite TV characters

friendship flower

What have you got in common with your favorite TV characters? Discover your fictional friendship connections.

1) Think of your two favorite TV characters.

2) Write your name in one of the spaces around the diagram, and their names in the other two.

3) Write something *unique* about each of you in the light-green segments.

4) In the mid-green segments, where the circles cross, write something that the two people represented by the circles have in common.

5) Finally, in the dark-green segment, write something all three of you have in common. It can be anything you like — eye color, home town, or favorite food!

6) Try creating celebrity friendship flowers for all your favorite TV characters and see what you have in common.

your name

character's name

character's name

what's your goal ?

Things I'll do before I'm
20

Things I'll do before I'm
30

Things I'll do before I'm
50

Things I'll do before I'm
100